I AM WONDERFUL

Written by Aesha LaViolette
Illustrated by Rubi Arbab & Sania Ahmed

I am beautiful. I am smart.
I can make a difference in the world.

I am God's child.

I have a purpose in life.

I love myself.

I have overcome obstacles.
When I make mistakes, I'll try and try again
until I am successful.

YES! I won.

I love my family and friends.

I will honor my mother and father.

I will always respect myself and other people.

4 + 4 =
Thank You

I will do my best in school.
I have a voice, and with that voice,
I will help make the world a better place.

I will never stop setting
and accomplishing goals.

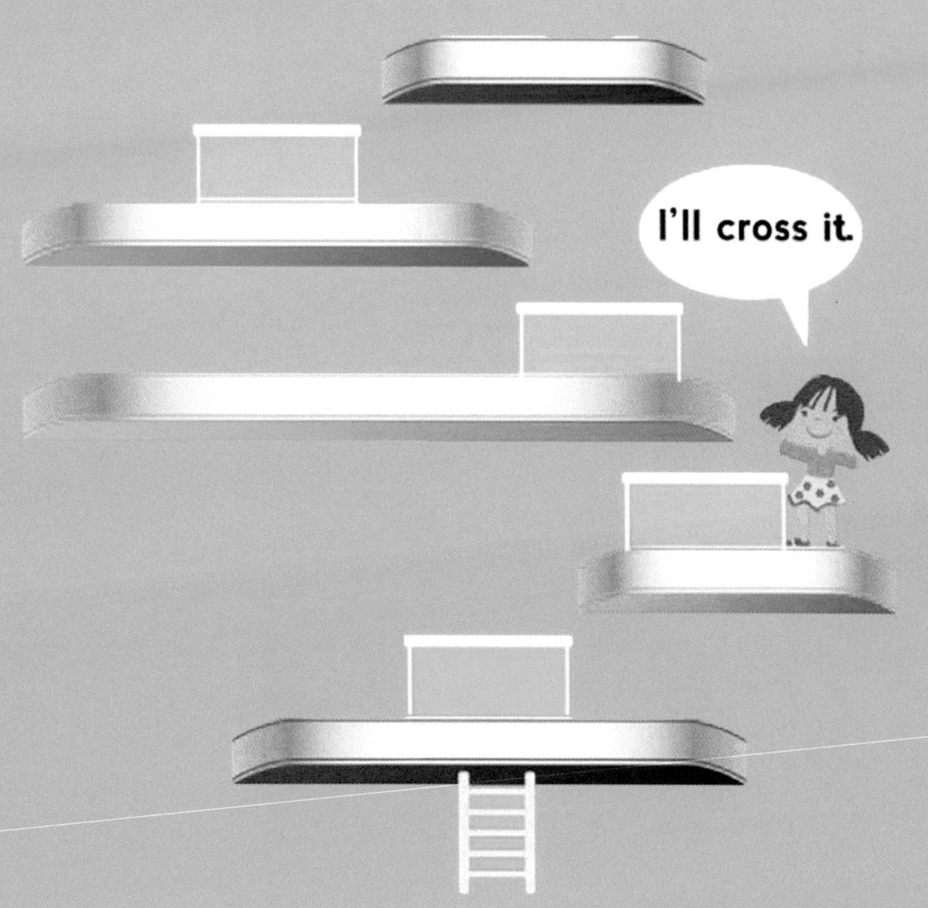
success
I'll cross it.

I am strong and creative.

I am a winner.

I will forgive the people who have hurt me.

I will be patient.

Beauty comes from within.

No matter how you look, and no matter how others think you look, you are beautiful.

Yes! I can do it.

Your size, race, class, and gender do not matter.
You are wonderful just the way God created you.

We are awesome.

Made in the USA
Columbia, SC
19 February 2020